GW00567900

A USEFUL DYSLEXIA HANDBOOK FOR ADULTS

I have been working with dyslexic adults for many years, in various capacities and through teaching basic skills to adults and post-school learners. I currently work in a local Further Education college, where my role is to assess potentially dyslexic learners across a wide age range, and to teach them using specialist methods. I also provide staff development sessions, to enable teaching staff to recognise dyslexia indicators and help their dyslexic students.

When I began teaching adults with specific reading and spelling difficulties in the early 1980's, the term dyslexia was rarely used, or it was sometimes viewed as an "excuse" for poor reading, writing and spelling. I can remember wondering, at that time, why a minority of adults with literacy difficulties did not learn how to read and spell like others, even though they were obviously bright and verbally articulate. It was then that my career-long interest in specific learning difficulties began.

I am often asked questions by people I meet who believe that dyslexia is causing their problems, and I have always wished that I could help a wider range of people than those with whom I come into regular contact. Then I had the idea of writing this book, so that I could reach as many people as possible, and help them to help themselves.

A USEFUL DYSLEXIA HANDBOOK FOR ADULTS

CATHERINE TAYLOR

A USEFUL DYSLEXIA HANDBOOK
FOR ADULTS

Olympia Publishers
London

www.olympiapublishers.com
OLYMPIA PAPERBACK EDITION

A CIP catalogue record for this title is
available from the British Library.

ISBN: 978-1-905513-60-4

First Published in 2008

Olympia Publishers
60 Cannon Street
London
EC4N 6NP

Printed in Great Britain

Dedication

For all the dyslexic people I have met over the years.
While I was teaching, I was also learning.

Acknowledgement

With special thanks to Julie for friendship, loyalty and unwavering support.

CONTENTS

WHO ARE YOU?

You may not know me. But I know you. I know every single one of you.

You are working in an office, breaking out in a cold sweat when the telephone rings and you're the only person around to take a written message for a colleague.

You are the young mother, resigned to your role at home and your low part-time earnings, simply because your reading and spelling are no good and it seems pointless even thinking about going in for anything better.

Or you might be the frustrated employee with a house, partner and family to support, heading up to the age of 40 after years of doing dead-end jobs which were extremely tedious and each lasted only a short time.

You could be the new college student, trying afresh after all the times you skipped your education in Years 10 and 11, because you learned to hate school and couldn't see any point in going.

Or are you the professional worker, happily demonstrating your competence through the lap-top on your desk with its voice-activated software? Marvellous – until the system fails, and you are floating in that bleak vacuum you dimly remember from before your technological days, wondering how you can cope now.

Many of you left school with average or poor exam grades or no passes at all, despite knowing you were bright. You might have excelled in practical skills, and worked at least as hard as – probably harder than – your peers. Maybe your self-esteem is low – and not just because your spelling is bad, your handwriting messy, and your reading slow and stilted. You have probably suffered years of humiliation in class by being unable to read aloud a piece of text put in front of you, or you were probably called *thick,* or *stupid,* or *lazy* by your teachers, who you think ought to know better.

You all have one thing in common. You are different. Your difficulties are unique to **you**. In the years I have worked with dyslexic learners, I can honestly say that I have not come across two people whose problems were exactly alike.

I have met you all, and many more. I have witnessed your struggles and frustrations, your despair over years of "ordinary" classes which did not help you. I have seen you break down in tears because at last, after all those years, you have met someone who finally *understands.* I have enjoyed seeing your confidence slowly grow once the door is opened, allowing light to pour in. You have suddenly realised that you *can* succeed. You have seized your opportunities, and started to fulfil your potential.

I have witnessed your joy as you learned to read, watched your thrill of discovering new information from books and websites. I have listened to you telling me you have read a story for the first time ever. I have taught you how to write out a cheque, and enjoyed seeing you take control of your own spending. I have seen your life slowly transform as you finally manage to do what you never thought you would – put your pen to paper, and write...

THE PURPOSE OF THIS BOOK

This handbook is not intended as a technical manual. There are plenty of excellent books, pamphlets and websites which will tell the seeker of knowledge everything he or she wants to know. I make no attempt to replicate what is already there.

I have written this book first and foremost for the dyslexic individual, to answer the questions I am often asked, and to offer some practical help for those whose lives are affected by dyslexia. The range is great, from the frustrated person who finds it hard to read and spell and thinks "they might be a bit dyslexic", to he or she whose life is completely blighted and spoiled, and who is unable to function on a daily basis, because of dyslexia.

Initially, I have aimed the handbook at adults and those who have passed the age of "compulsory" education.

Older readers might have had a raw deal in their educational years, in the times before dyslexia was fully recognised. As youngsters with these specific difficulties, they might have been "written off" and failed by the system.

The new school leaver could have had an equally tough time, and is perhaps wondering why, after attending school for so many years, he or she is still struggling to read and spell.

Other people will want to read this book, and I hope they will enjoy it and learn from it. They will include relatives, partners and friends of dyslexic people, their educational support workers and tutors, professionals with whom they come into contact...in fact anyone with an interest in dyslexia who wants to *know*, but not to study the subject deeply.

I have explained things in simple terms, as I do in the everyday face-to-face situation, and I hope that this will help you to make sense of your dyslexia, or give some understanding of those dyslexic people with whom your life is connected.

WHAT IS DYSLEXIA?

Dyslexia is a condition which most of us associate simply with a difficulty in reading and spelling.

It is a group of symptoms which manifest as a specific difficulty with the processing of information and written language, and is therefore perhaps at its most visible in these activities, but the impact of dyslexia is much wider than many people realise. Amongst other things it can affect:

- Reading

- Spelling

- Handwriting

- Organisation

- Getting ideas down onto paper

- Telling left from right

- Visual perception

- Short-term memory

- Memorising number sequences, facts, appointments and so on.

- Following instructions

Dyslexia ranges along a continuum from mild to severe and all the shades in between. It is very "individual" – each person tends to be affected in a different way.

It bears no relation to intelligence. Despite their poor literacy skills, dyslexic people – perhaps because of their holistic ways of thinking - are very often extremely bright, creative, orally articulate, ingenious and highly successful in their own spheres. For example, think of such famous people as Winston Churchill, Einstein, Henry Ford, Walt Disney, Agatha Christie, Alexander Graham Bell, Leonardo da Vinci, and others far too numerous to mention. Thus, dyslexia can be seen as a "gift" which enables people to think in a different way, as well as being a disadvantage.

Unfortunately, dyslexia in an individual sometimes goes undetected and unrecognised. This was very much the case in the past, so that dyslexic adults often had very unpleasant learning experiences as children and were "written off" by the education system, or told that they were lazy, or stupid, or both. Such negative early experiences can and do have serious or damaging consequences, and can result in low confidence and self-esteem. This, combined with the practical and academic difficulties involved, often results in an unwillingness to engage in activities requiring the use of written language and creates an obvious barrier to learning and carrying out basic tasks at work.

What do the experts have to say about dyslexia, and what dyslexia actually is?

Here is the British Dyslexia Association definition of dyslexia:

Dyslexia is a specific learning difficulty which is neurobiological in origin and persists across the lifespan.

It is characterised by difficulties with phonological processing, rapid naming, working memory, processing speed and the automatic development of skills that are unexpected in relation to an individual's other cognitive abilities.

These processing difficulties can undermine the acquisition of literacy and numeracy skills, as well as musical notation, and have an effect on verbal communication, organisation and adaptation to change.

Their impact can be mitigated by correct teaching, strategy development and the use of information technology.

...and here is the definition from Dyslexia Action (formerly the Dyslexia Institute):

Dyslexia is a specific learning difficulty that mainly affects reading and spelling. Dyslexia is characterized by difficulties in processing word-sounds and by

weakness of short-term verbal memory; its effects may be seen in spoken language as well as written language. The current evidence suggests that these difficulties arise from inefficiencies in language-processing areas in the left hemisphere of the brain which, in turn, appear to be linked to genetic differences.

Dyslexia is life-long, but its effects can be minimised by targeted literacy intervention, technological support and adaptations to ways of working and learning. Dyslexia varies in severity and often occurs alongside other specific learning difficulties, such as Dyspraxia or Attention Deficit Disorder, resulting in variation in the degree and nature of individuals' strengths and weaknesses.

Now, let's put the definitions aside for while - excellent and accurate though they are. I will explain dyslexia in a straightforward and simple way that hopefully you will be able to understand and relate to.

READING AND SPELLING

Reading and spelling are two of the most complex tasks that your brain is likely to be required to do. Why is this?

Without delving too deeply into the complexities of the brain and the way in which it processes language, let's take a look at what happens when you read. Considering that human beings are expected to be able to read fluently from an early age, it can't be too difficult. Or can it?

Let us imagine that the alphabet as we know it suddenly has to be scrapped. The government says we can't use it any more. So we need to find a new way to turn the sounds we make, that is our spoken language, into marks and squiggles on a piece of paper, so that people can record what they want to say, and so that other people will know what has been recorded.

We will start simply:

gives us the sound of **a**, that we hear in cat.

▢ gives us the sound of **b**, that we hear in bus.

Δ gives us the sound of **c**, that we have in cat (although we also have an entirely different symbol, ≡ (k), which gives us the same sound).

⊗ gives us the sound of **d**, that we have in dog.

→ gives us the sound of **e**, that we have in egg.

ɘ gives us the sound of **t**, that we have in cat.

So far, so good. Already we can write down a few short words to read. Try these:

▢#⊗

▢→⊗

⊗#▢

Δ#▢

Δ# ɘ

Did you manage to work them out? It is likely that, at first, you had to look at each symbol, but by around the third or fourth "word" you were beginning to remember the sound of each symbol, or "letter".

We decide to record on paper the sounds we know as **"cat"**. The problem is, do we begin with the symbol Δ or

27

≡, both of which give us the same sound? There is no possible way of knowing this, but...! You've seen this word before, so you draw on your memory, and remember that it was recorded as Δ#ɔ. You form a picture of this in your mind, so that you can draw on it again for future use.

Now we decide to record the sounds we use for a very nice bright colour, the colour of poppies and post-boxes and holly berries. That's an easy one: ↓→⊗.

This spelling thing looks easy, doesn't it? Once we know the symbols to represent the sounds, we can just join them together, and instantly we have a "word"! Wonderful!

Okay, so from knowing ↓→⊗ as that nice bright colour, we can also write down the sounds for that filling food we all eat, the one that we cut into slices and make into sandwiches, which must be □↓→⊗ (bred). Easy! However, someone is now telling us that although we've got the symbols correct for the *sound*, this word has an entirely different meaning! Oh dear! For the foodstuff, we have to use □↓→#⊗ (bread). Again, we will have to remember the difference between these two words for the next time we need to use either of them. Getting complicated, isn't it? And there's much, much more yet to come!

We've now grasped that words can sound the same, but are written down differently. We have also learned that →# (ea) in the word □↓→#⊗ (bread) has a sound exactly like the → in ↓→⊗, that very nice bright colour. So how should we pronounce ↓→#⊗? It seems safe to assume that it is similar in sound to □↓→#⊗, the nice thing we like to eat. Some expert is telling us that it can do, but it also has another sound, like →→. It has a slightly different sound in the word →#↓ (ear). And →#↓ has different sounds in the word !→#↓ɘ (heart) and →#↓ɘ! (earth).

Confusing? Let's leave that for now, and look at a very different aspect of spelling, the letter 's', which we will depict as ↔.

In a word such as Δ#ɘ (cat), adding ↔ gives us a whole new concept. Instead of one Δ#ɘ, we are now recording the idea of two, three or even many Δ#ɘ↔. This again seems simple enough. It is also creative. We can have lots of Δ#ɘ↔ (cats), ⊗⊕∇↔ (dogs), □→⊗↔ (beds) and so on.

We can see that adding ↔ to a *naming* word (noun) tells us that there are more than one. If ↔ is added to a *doing* or *being* word (verb) it actually helps us to distinguish which type of person is doing the action, for example ∅ ↓→#⊗(I read) but □⊕□ ↓→#⊗↔ (Bob reads). If we put another symbol (') in front of the ↔, for example ⊗⊕∇'↔ (dog's), it now tells us that something belongs to the ⊗⊕∇. Things are becoming more and more complicated.

To go back to the symbol ↔ when it is used to show *more than one*, or a *plural*, we have further bewilderment when someone points out that we cannot have □◊↔↔ (the plural of bus) or ∩#≈↔ (the plural of fax), because these words, and many others, end in a hissing sound, and therefore must have →↔ (es) as their plural. Then there are other rules for plurals, such as words ending in ∉ (y) which either take ↔ to make them into a plural, or drop their ∉ and add ∅→↔ (ies), depending on whether the letter before the ∉ is a vowel or a consonant.

There are also completely different rules for plurals, such as one ɘ⊕⊕ɘ! (tooth) but three ɘ→→ɘ! and one ∨⊕◊↔→ (mouse) but six ∨∅Δ→. If ∨⊕◊↔→ (mouse) becomes ∨∅Δ→, however, then why is it that !⊕◊↔→ (house) does not become !∅Δ→?

Here's another peculiar aspect of spelling for you to think about. "ɘ∅⊕∞" is a word ending that gives us a completely new sound, like "shun". If we sound out the individual letters, it sounds like "tie-on". How can this be? It seems difficult. Yet once you remember the sound and appearance of this combination you can use it to help you read and spell many words. The only problem is that some spellings, for example *mansion*, use –sion (or ↔∅⊕∞). There is no rule for choosing which of these endings to use; again, it is a case of remembering the picture of the "word", which is not at all easy, especially when letters are similar in appearance, such as →, ↔, ↓, or ⊗, ⊕.

You can perhaps see, from this, just a fraction of all that your brain has to do in order to read and spell. It is a combination of:

(i)   Knowing the sound of each symbol.

(ii)   Linking the sounds of the different symbols together.

(iii)   Remembering what the words and symbols look like.

There are further complications that we have not even begun to touch on. For example, remember that once you have learned all the symbols of our "new" alphabet, you must learn equivalent symbols which represent capital letters – and venture into another area of written language called "punctuation". Some of these capital letters are simply larger versions of their small counterparts, such as o/O, p/P, s/S. Others such as e/E, g/G, n/N, q/Q, r/R, t/T, are entirely different in appearance.

De-coding and encoding

Here is a complete list of our "new" alphabet:

a	#	n	∞
b	□	o	⊕
c	Δ	p	Ψ
d	⊗	q	+
e	→	r	↓
f	∩	s	↔
g	∇	t	∋
h	!	u	◊
i	∅	v	•
j	Ω	w	↑
k	≡	x	≈
l	◆	y	∉
m	∨	z	*

Can you work out what these spellings are? (Answers at end of chapter)

1. +◊→→∞

2. #ΨΨ♦→

3. Δ#↓#•#∞

4. →♦→Ψ!#∞ɘ

5. →⊗∅∞□◊↓∇!

6. ɘ→♦→Ψ!⊕∞→

7. ɘ→♦→•∅↔∅⊕∞

8. ɘ→♦→∇↓#Ψ!

9. *⊕⊕↔

10. #ΨΨ♦→↔

It is very possible that when you were doing this activity two things happened:

Firstly, as you worked out the word, after a few letters you will have had an idea of what the word was going to be. This is because you were both predicting, from your existing knowledge, what the construction of the word was, and also building up the sounds as you went along.

Secondly, you probably began to recognise where there was a repeating element, for example at the start of words 6, 7 and 8. This is because you were using sight recognition of the words.

Now, let's try this the other way round. Can you convert these words into the "new" alphabet? (Answers at end of chapter)

1.   desk

2.   weather

3.   table

4.   computer

5.   Manchester

6.   heather

7.   company

8.   glasses

9.   information

10.   activity

Did this feel harder than decoding the first list of words? Again, as the task progressed, it is likely that you began to remember which "letters" to use for which sound. You also perhaps realised that you needed to use the same four "letters" to begin the words 4 and 7, and that apart from the first "letter", 2 and 6 were the same.

You can perhaps see that in order to do these two tasks, you need to know the sound of each letter, be able to link the sounds together, and remember what the symbols and "words" look like.

If you have problems doing this, reading and spelling will be difficult for you. This might help to show how reading and spelling are difficult for dyslexic people.

It might also be hard for some people to physically represent the letters onto the page. Their hand and their use of the pen might refuse to do what their eyes and brain are telling them to do. Let's explain all this in terms of dyslexia.

Answers to "new alphabet" questions

Spellings

1. queen
2. apple
3. caravan
4. elephant
5. Edinburgh
6. telephone
7. television
8. telegraph
9. zoos
10. apples

"New" alphabet spellings

1. $\otimes \rightarrow \leftrightarrow \equiv$
2. $\uparrow \rightarrow \# \ni \, ! \rightarrow \downarrow$
3. $\ni \# \square \blacklozenge \rightarrow$
4. $\Delta \oplus \vee \Psi \lozenge \ni \rightarrow \downarrow$
5. $\vee \# \infty \Delta \, ! \rightarrow \leftrightarrow \ni \rightarrow \downarrow$
6. $! \rightarrow \# \ni \, ! \rightarrow \downarrow$
7. $\Delta \oplus \vee \Psi \# \infty \notin$
8. $\nabla \blacklozenge \# \leftrightarrow \leftrightarrow \rightarrow \leftrightarrow$
9. $\varnothing \infty \cap \oplus \downarrow \vee \# \ni \varnothing \otimes \infty$
10. $\# \Delta \ni \varnothing \bullet \varnothing \ni \notin$

THE CAUSES OF DYSLEXIA

Here we have an immense issue, one which has been occupying experts for many years. There are different theories on the causes of dyslexia, and research is ongoing.

Investigation has shown that there is a difference in the structure of the brain in dyslexic as opposed to non-dyslexic persons or individuals, especially in the language centres. Attempts have been made to isolate where, exactly, the dyslexic problem lies, but researchers have not yet established which part of the brain is responsible for the difficulties.

Conclusive agreement about the causes of dyslexia has not yet been reached. There are different views as to whether the basis of dyslexia lies in biological factors which cause problems with phonological processing (that is, the processing of sounds in language), "timing" difficulties relating to information processing, visual processing difficulties – or more than one of these.

There is agreement however that hereditary factors do play a major part in the existence of dyslexia, so that it tends to occur in genetic family groups. If any other members of your family are affected in this way, it is possible that you might be as well.

DYSLEXIA PROCESSING PROBLEMS

To understand the difficulties that dyslexic people have with written language, you need to know the three main types of processing problems they have. These are:

Visual processing problems

Auditory processing problems

Motor processing problems

Let me explain these in a little more detail. You can also relate back to your experiments with the "new" alphabet to understand what happens with each of these difficulties.

Visual processing problems

Dyslexic people with these difficulties find it hard to remember and recognise the shape and appearance of words, and therefore often mis-read a word as something visually very similar, which results in a complete loss of meaning of what a piece of text is about. For example, they might read: "could" **instead of** "cloud", or "summer" **for** "simmer".

People with these difficulties will try to work out words from the sounds of the letters, which can make reading very hard for them, often slow, jerky and disjointed. They may frequently lose their place when reading, often "skipping" words or lines, or perhaps reading the same line twice.

They will also tend to spell phonetically, which means that irregular spelling patterns are particularly troublesome for them. Their spellings will often contain reversed letters, such as "brian" for "brain", "was" for "saw", "wirting" for "writing".

Auditory processing problems

The difficulty here is in matching the letter sounds to the letter or word on the page. People with these problems will have great difficulty using phonic methods of learning to read or spell. Instead, they will tend to use context clues in the passage they are reading and attempt to memorise the visual pattern of words, often making an incorrect "guess" from the sense of the other words in the sentence.

Spellings by these people sometimes look very strange indeed, for example "evenlop" for "envelope", "devlop" for "develop" and "hotspal" for "hospital". This is because people with these problems mis-interpret and confuse sounds, often missing them out altogether.

Motor processing problems

Dyslexic people with these problems tend to have difficulty with handwriting, which may appear messy and untidy. Letters will often be poorly formed, and there may be problems with controlling the pen.

Spelling problems caused by motor processing difficulties are usually characterised either by the repetition of syllables, for example "instititution" for "institution", or the contraction of words, e.g. "rember" for "remember", or "phenomon" for "phenomenon".

Organisational problems, which can have far-reaching consequences, can also arise from motor processing difficulties. In written language these manifest as a difficulty with planning writing and organising information needed for written work and keeping workfiles in order.

For people with these problems, a piece of writing will contain all the required information, but it may appear fragmented and out of order. Files and folders will typically have sheets "all over the place" and in no logical sequence.

AM I DYSLEXIC?

Without an assessment being carried out, it is impossible to say for certain whether or not your problems are being caused by dyslexia. However, there is a range of factors which, put together, will make it **likely** that this is causing your difficulties.

If you come from a family where one or more of your blood relatives is dyslexic, this will increase the possibility that dyslexia is causing your reading, writing and spelling difficulties, and you will also probably recognise the same – or similar – problems. If you are dyslexic you are probably good at activities which do not involve written language, but you may have trouble with reading or putting pen to paper.

To help you to get an idea of whether dyslexia **might** be causing your problems, here is a checklist. A large number of indicators **do not say that you are dyslexic**; only that there is **a strong possibility** that this is causing your problems.

DYSLEXIA CHECKLIST FOR ADULTS

Tick the box if you have answered 'YES' to the question.

1. Do you have trouble telling left from right? ☐

2. Is it hard for you to read a map? ☐

3. Do you get lost easily? ☐

4. Do you have trouble with saying long words? ☐

5. Do you have trouble "finding the word you want"? ☐

6. Do you have trouble taking telephone messages and passing them on? ☐

7. Do you have trouble remembering telephone numbers? ☐

8. Do you get number sequences mixed up? ☐

9. Do you mix up dates and appointments? ☐

10. Do you get the months and seasons mixed up? ☐

11. Do you find it hard to follow written instructions? ☐

12. Do you have trouble remembering where you have put things? ☐

13. Do you find it hard to remember the order of the alphabet? ☐

14. Do you find it hard to remember multiplication tables? ☐

15. Are you a slow reader? ☐

16. Do you find it hard to remember what you have read? ☐

17. Do you find it hard to understand what you have read? ☐

18. Do you avoid reading aloud? ☐

19. Do you have trouble concentrating on small print?

20. Is your spelling poor? ☐

21. Do you spell with the right letters but in the wrong order? ☐

22. Can you spell a word one day and forget it the next? ☐

23. Do you write letters back to front? ☐

24. Is your writing untidy? ☐

25. Is filling in forms hard for you? ☐

26. Is it hard for you to organise things on paper? ☐

27. Do you forget things quickly? ☐

28. Do you find it hard to concentrate when listening to a talk? ☐

29. Do you get distracted by background noise? ☐

30. Is your time hard to organise? ☐

If you have ticked more than half of these, it could be that you are dyslexic, and you should seek further advice.

ASSESSMENT

A full diagnosis of dyslexia can only be made by an Educational Psychologist or suitably qualified Specialist Dyslexia Tutor, but a range of tests are available to people working in this area which they can use to form a reliable judgement about the likelihood of dyslexia.

Initial screening

This usually begins with an interview to put the person at ease, form a rapport and establish very important **background information** such as:

- school history

- family literacy background

- language and listening skills

- medical facts

- short-term and auditory memory

- spatial awareness

- numerical ability

This may be followed by:

Reading assessment

Establishes reading style, reading speed, reading comprehension, tracking ability, word attack skills and a detailed analysis to determine the type of errors made.

Writing/spelling assessment through dictation

This gives an analysis of writing speed, pen hold and paper position, handwriting and punctuation problems and also spelling error rate. It provides a detailed analysis of spelling error types to identify problems with visual processing, auditory processing, problems with spelling patterns and spelling rules, as well as identifying visuo-spatial and visuo-motor difficulties.

If you simply wish to know if dyslexia is likely to be causing your problems, initial screening may be all that is needed. Other tests which, depending on the situation, might be used instead of, or in addition to, a preliminary assessment are:

DAST (Psychological Corporation) – Dyslexia Adult Screening Test

This is comprised of a series of 11 sub-tests which assess:

a) Rapid object naming ability (to test word retrieval and speed of information processing)

b) Reading

c) Postural stability

d) Phonemic awareness

e) Spelling

f) Auditory memory

g) Nonsense-word reading (to test phonic skills)

h) Non-verbal reasoning

i) Writing skills

j) Verbal reasoning and fluency

k) Semantic reasoning and fluency

Analysis of results is done through scoring via a chart and graph, which shows a "Dyslexia At Risk Factor" of 1 to 3 in each area, and an overall "Dyslexia At Risk Quotient" where 1.0 or above can be said to be strongly indicative of the presence of dyslexia.

PPVT-III Vocabulary Tests

This is a useful test to assess language skills in the area of verbal reasoning and vocabulary development.

Scoring results are calculated through a series of tables which show Age Equivalent, Standardised Score and percentile statistics.

WRAT Reading, Spelling and Arithmetic tests

These tests measure reading accuracy, spelling accuracy and mathematical ability. The results have high validity and reliability factors, give standardised scores and percentile statistics, and can be used to give an Age Equivalent.

Full assessment

Literacy tests

A wider range of tests is used for a fuller assessment, some of which are listed above. They are to measure some or all of the following features of literacy skills:

- Word recognition

- Reading accuracy

- Reading speed

- Reading comprehension

- Spelling accuracy

- Writing speed

Other tests

Where a need is perceived, these can be selected individually from an available range to fit the situation and the person being assessed. They can test such skills as alphabet recognition, sequencing skills, letter-sound correspondence, phonic awareness, reading and spelling ability, auditory memory, speed of processing, verbal reasoning and non-verbal reasoning.

Cognitive tests

These are tests of general intellectual ability such as the Weschler Adult Intelligence Scale tests (WAIS-III), or Wide Range Intelligence Tests (WRIT).

The reason behind administering this type of test is to make a comparison of the person's performance in the literacy tasks and the general ability tasks. As we have already seen, reading and writing are highly complex skills; if a person is of average or high intellectual ability, we could normally safely assume that they would be able to apply this intelligence to learning to read and spell. Poor scores in the literacy tasks and good scores in the general ability tasks would usually suggest a dyslexic profile – hence we have a "portrait" of the person who is articulate, bright and often excels at practical or other skills, yet struggles with the basics of reading, writing and spelling.

It should be pointed out, however, that having below average general ability does not rule out the possibility of dyslexia, but this might make it harder to identify.

SELF-HELP

If you are dyslexic, the best help you can have is some specialised tuition on a one-to-one basis for help with your reading, writing and spelling.

For everyday activities, there are a number of things you can do to help yourself. These tips will not take the place of having a tutor, but may make life a bit easier.

Print size

Very small print, for example Times New Roman, size 12 and under, is hard for many people to read, but especially dyslexic readers. If you are reading from a book or magazine, a magnifying glass or magnifying spectacles will help. Font size 14 upwards is generally more satisfactory for dyslexic people.

Using a line marker

Rows of close print are difficult for dyslexic readers to cope with. You can use a solid ruler under the lines as you read down the page, or make a simple "line marker" with a piece of card.

Tinted paper

Reading and writing are better for most dyslexic people on non-white paper. Obviously it is not always possible to copy printed text onto tinted paper, but if there is an option it is worth doing.

When writing you have a choice! If you have been screened for Scotopic Sensitivity Syndrome (see page 46-47) you will have an idea of the best coloured paper to use. Otherwise try cream or pale blue or grey – they should all improve things.

Font style

Certain font styles are much easier for dyslexic people to read and use on the computer. Arial, comic sans, sans serif are all good. If you are writing onto the computer and there is a requirement for a particular format, e.g. Times New Roman, Size 12, remember that you can do your piece of writing in a size and style of **your choice** and change this when your text is completed.

Computers

The computer word-processor is good for writing. It will improve the appearance of text and presentation of work, as well as providing a spelling and grammar check and developing motor skills. It is better to turn down the brightness and contrast of the screen.

A tinted background is generally better than the glare of white on your computer screen page. If you have been tested for Scotopic Sensitivity Syndrome (see page 46-

47), you will know the best colours to select, otherwise some experimentation may be needed.

In Microsoft it is fairly easy to change the background colour of your Word documents, Outlook Express and e-mails, Internet Explorer and so on. Here's how to do it:

Start

Settings

Control panel

Appearance and themes

Change the desktop background

Appearance

Advanced

Item

Window

Colour grid – other

(Select the colour you want – then ok)

If reading from the computer screen, do not struggle with very small text. Simply highlight it and change it to a font size and style which is more comfortable for you. If the right edge of the text is justified - that is, if it has a straight edge – highlight the text and unjustify the right edge. Text with an unjustified right margin edge is much easier on the eye.

Dictaphones

A Dictaphone can be useful for recording ideas quickly to write down later, also for recording a talk or lecture.

Essential needs

To start with, focus on learning skills that you *need* – writing a cheque, making lists of local place names, sending a greetings card. It will help to look at examples of how to do this – study cards and letters that you have received, ask someone to complete a sample cheque for you and so on.

Using a "model"

Look at a format of how to put a letter together – where your address needs to go, what information to put in it and so on.

If you are writing longer pieces such as essays, again look at a good essay and see how it has been put together and presented.

Reading level

Do not try reading text which is too hard for you – read something at a level you feel comfortable with, which will be much more enjoyable and develop your fluency. There are plenty of "easy readers" available, but if you do not have access to these, don't be afraid of reading children's books. Many of them are entertaining and compelling - and enjoyed even by good readers!

Books and tapes

Books with accompanying tapes are excellent for dyslexic readers.

A-Z notebook

A small notebook indexed A-Z is very useful for recording words which are difficult or which are needed regularly. (Make sure they are spelled correctly!)

Spell-checkers

You can use the computer for checking spelling in word-processed text. For everyday use, a pocket spell-checker is a useful, inexpensive tool to carry around with you.

Spelling

A full spelling method is shown below, but generally you might find it helpful to break long words, whether reading or writing, into smaller "chunks" that you feel you can cope with. Look at print around yourself and try to see "words within words" and small pieces of words, for example:

tele-phone

kit-chen

com-put-er

If you do this, you will begin to see patterns which repeat in words, such as:

l-ight

f-ight

n-ight

s-ight

You will also learn to identify beginnings and endings which can be used for many words. For example, **–tion** is used in words such as:

sta-tion

na-tion

informa-tion;

"-un" is used to begin words such as:

un-happy

un-done

un-fasten

and many others.

"-ing" is added to the end of lots and lots of words:

sing-ing

read-ing

walk-ing

…and so on. (NOTE: With some word endings the root words change slightly.)

Spelling method

A full range of spelling exercises can be found in a companion book, "A Useful Handbook for Dyslexic Spellers", but there is a basic method with which you can help yourself to spell. Here it is:

Think of between six and ten words that you use regularly and that you **know** you have trouble spelling.

List them here.

1 ………………………   2 ……………………………

3 ………………………   4 ……………………………

5 ………………………   6 ……………………………

7 ………………………   8 ……………………………

9 ………………………   10 ……………………………

Ask someone who is good at spelling to check them and list any corrections at the side. Alternatively, you can find them in a dictionary, or use your computer spell-checker or a pocket spell-checker.

We are now going to split the words up into chunks.

People like to do this in different ways, depending on how they learn. It is important to split them up in a way that suits you, so you need to try a few different ways.

For example, a lot of people struggle with the word **"information"**.

These are different ways of splitting it, or you might have another way you like better:

in-for-mat-ion

in-form-at-ion

in-for-ma-tion

in-form-a-tion

Or we can try with another word, **"sincerely",** which causes a lot of problems for people:

sin-cere-ly

sin-cer-ely

s-inc-ere-ly

sinc-er-el-y

since-rely

Get the idea? Now split your own words into chunks.

You need to make a clear list showing first your words, then the way you have split them. It will look something like this:

develop	de-ve-lop
Wednesday	Wed-nes-day
furniture	fur-nit-ure
university	uni-ver-sit-y
convenient	con-veni-ent
necessary	nec-ess-ary

This is the basic method for learning your words:

Look, Say, Cover, Write, Check.

…and this is how it's done:

- Look at the word and say it at the same time. If you are on your own, do it out loud. Keep doing this until you feel sure of the spelling.

- Cover the word up, then try writing it down.

- Check to see if you have spelled it correctly.

All of these steps are very important. Do not miss them out.

If you get a word wrong, try again!

Try to spend ten minutes or so each day – more than once if you wish - on this activity. If you are feeling tired with it, put it away and come back later.

At the end of a week, ask someone to test you on the spellings.

If you have got them right, try using each one in a sentence. If you have not yet learned a word, it can simply go into a new list.

You are now ready for a fresh list of spellings, but keep on using the ones you have learned!

SCOTOPIC SENSITIVITY SYNDROME

This condition is also known as Irlen's Syndrome. It usually – but not always - co-exists with dyslexia and other specific learning difficulties.

It is a **visual perception** difficulty rather than a processing problem, and is best understood as a sensitivity to white light - so that people with this condition have difficulty with the contrast of black print on white or glossy paper, and often struggle to read in fluorescent or bright lighting and from computer screens.

Scotopic dyslexic individuals are often helped by using a coloured plastic overlay, which can stop letters from appearing to float around, move off the page, create white "print rivers" and so on; and prevent the headaches, eye soreness and other symptoms and difficulties which are produced by reading from white paper for these people.

Scotopic Sensitivity Syndrome is not a difficulty with learning, and it is unlikely to be detected through normal eyesight tests. Indicators may be noticed and identified during dyslexia screening, but the tasks administered in dyslexia assessment will not, in themselves, test for Scotopic Sensitivity Syndrome.

Using the Irlen method, the condition is diagnosed through a series of perceptual tasks, followed by further testing to determine and provide the correct colour of overlay. Glasses can also be prescribed, but these are not always the same tint as the overlay. Using tinted paper also tends to be helpful.

Testing needs to be done formally, as giving the wrong tint of paper, plastic overlay and/or glasses can do more harm than good.

Alternative methods of testing include the use of technological equipment which, again, provides a range of overlay tints and gives fine selections of colour combination for the screen background of the computer.

It is worth noting that non-dyslexic individuals can also have Scotopic Sensitivity Syndrome.

A FINAL WORD

I hope you have enjoyed reading this book, and that it has helped you to understand your dyslexia, or the problems faced by a dyslexic person you know. I also hope that the book has given you some ideas on how to tackle your difficulties and how to help yourself in a practical way with your reading, writing and spelling.

This brings us to the end of the handbook, but for you – or someone close to you – it could be the beginning of a new way of looking at dyslexia, the start of a means to address your problems, and the gateway to making achievements that you might not previously have thought possible.

Here are some suggestions as to how you can take a further step forward, and open the door to opportunity.

Learning and study support
There are places in every area where you can go to classes to improve your literacy skills, which include dyslexic difficulties. You will be able, and be encouraged, to improve your reading and spelling, and you will have the opportunity to take exams in literacy and move on to further and higher levels of learning.

Do not feel that you cannot take a mainstream course of study because of your dyslexia. Colleges of

Further Education have a learning support department, to help if you are struggling with the written aspects of a course. They will probably assess you for dyslexia if you, and they, think that this is causing your problems. They will certainly support you with your studies. They will make arrangements for any special help you might need in your exams such as extra time, a reader, and someone to write down your answers for you.

Speak out
Although you might have been hiding your reading and spelling problems for a long time, dyslexia is nothing at all to be ashamed of. When you start to tell people that you are dyslexic you will be surprised at how many others "open up" to you, who might also have been covering up their difficulties.

If you tell your employers that you are dyslexic they will probably make allowances for you in your working practice. If your dyslexia is severe, an employer has a legal obligation under the Disability Discrimination Act to make "reasonable adjustments" to the way in which you work.

Follow your dream
Remember those well-known dyslexic people I mentioned, and the remarkable achievements they have all made in life? If they can succeed, so can you. Make a list of all the famous dyslexic people you can find. It will inspire you. Tell yourself: **"I can"**.

And lastly…
I wish you success in everything you do in your life.
Overcome your dyslexia; do not let it overcome you.
Decide what you want to do - and go for it.
Good luck!

Catherine Taylor

FURTHER READING AND HELP ORGANISATIONS

Suggested further reading

The Gift of Dyslexia by Ronald D. Davis (Souvenir Press, first published 1994)

Making Dyslexia Work for You by Vicki Goodwin & Bonita Thomson (David Fulton, 2004)

Help Organisations
British Dyslexia Association
www.bdadyslexia.org.uk

Dyslexia Action (formerly Dyslexia Institute)
www.dyslexiaaction.org.uk

Adult Dyslexia Organisation
www.adult-dyslexia.org.uk

Irlen Institute
www.irlen.com

The Davis Dyslexia Organisation
www.dyslexia.com